Materials Characterisation IV

Computational Methods
and Experiments

WITPRESS

WIT Press publishes leading books in Science and Technology.
Visit our website for new and current list of titles.
www.witpress.com

WITeLibrary

Home of the Transactions of the Wessex Institute.
Papers presented at Materials Characterisation IV are archived in the WIT eLibrary
in volume 64 of WIT Transactions on Engineering Sciences (ISSN 1743-3533).
The WIT eLibrary provides the international scientific community with immediate
and permanent access to individual papers presented at WIT conferences.
http://library.witpress.com

FOURTH INTERNATIONAL CONFERENCE ON
COMPUTATIONAL METHODS AND EXPERIMENTS IN
MATERIALS CHARACTERISATION

MATERIALS CHARACTERISATION 2009

CONFERENCE CHAIRMEN

A.A. Mammoli
University of New Mexico, USA

C.A. Brebbia
Wessex Institute of Technology, UK

INTERNATIONAL SCIENTIFIC ADVISORY COMMITTEE

A. Bayton
A. Benavent-Climent
S. Bordere
A. Galybin
H. Huh
A.J. Klemm
J. Phillips

P. Prochazka
I. Sanchez
A. Staroselsky
H. Toda
A.D.G. Tsonos
P. Viot

Organised by
Wessex Institute of Technology, UK
and
University of New Mexico, USA

Sponsored by
WIT Transactions on Engineering Sciences

WIT Transactions

Transactions Editor

Carlos Brebbia
Wessex Institute of Technology
Ashurst Lodge, Ashurst
Southampton SO40 7AA, UK
Email: carlos@wessex.ac.uk

Editorial Board

K G Goulias Pennsylvania State University, USA

F Grandori Politecnico di Milano, Italy

W E Grant Texas A & M University, USA

S Grilli University of Rhode Island, USA

R H J Grimshaw, Loughborough University, UK

D Gross Technische Hochschule Darmstadt, Germany

R Grundmann Technische Universitat Dresden, Germany

A Gualtierotti IDHEAP, Switzerland

R C Gupta National University of Singapore, Singapore

J M Hale University of Newcastle, UK

K Hameyer Katholieke Universiteit Leuven, Belgium

C Hanke Danish Technical University, Denmark

K Hayami National Institute of Informatics, Japan

Y Hayashi Nagoya University, Japan

L Haydock Newage International Limited, UK

A H Hendrickx Free University of Brussels, Belgium

C Herman John Hopkins University, USA

S Heslop University of Bristol, UK

I Hideaki Nagoya University, Japan

D A Hills University of Oxford, UK

W F Huebner Southwest Research Institute, USA

J A C Humphrey Bucknell University, USA

M Y Hussaini Florida State University, USA

W Hutchinson Edith Cowan University, Australia

T H Hyde University of Nottingham, UK

M Iguchi Science University of Tokyo, Japan

D B Ingham University of Leeds, UK

L Int Panis VITO Expertisecentrum IMS, Belgium

N Ishikawa National Defence Academy, Japan

J Jaafar UiTm, Malaysia

W Jager Technical University of Dresden, Germany

Y Jaluria Rutgers University, USA

C M Jefferson University of the West of England, UK

P R Johnston Griffith University, Australia

D R H Jones University of Cambridge, UK

N Jones University of Liverpool, UK

D Kaliampakos National Technical University of Athens, Greece

N Kamiya Nagoya University, Japan

D L Karabalis University of Patras, Greece

M Karlsson Linkoping University, Sweden

T Katayama Doshisha University, Japan

K L Katsifarakis Aristotle University of Thessaloniki, Greece

J T Katsikadelis National Technical University of Athens, Greece

E Kausel Massachusetts Institute of Technology, USA

H Kawashima The University of Tokyo, Japan

B A Kazimee Washington State University, USA

S Kim University of Wisconsin-Madison, USA

D Kirkland Nicholas Grimshaw & Partners Ltd, UK

E Kita Nagoya University, Japan

A S Kobayashi University of Washington, USA

T Kobayashi University of Tokyo, Japan

D Koga Saga University, Japan

A Konrad University of Toronto, Canada

S Kotake University of Tokyo, Japan

A N Kounadis National Technical University of Athens, Greece

W B Kratzig Ruhr Universitat Bochum, Germany

T Krauthammer Penn State University, USA

C-H Lai University of Greenwich, UK

M Langseth Norwegian University of Science and Technology, Norway

B S Larsen Technical University of Denmark, Denmark

F Lattarulo, Politecnico di Bari, Italy

A Lebedev Moscow State University, Russia

L J Leon University of Montreal, Canada

D Lewis Mississippi State University, USA

S lghobashi University of California Irvine, USA

K-C Lin University of New Brunswick, Canada

A A Liolios Democritus University of Thrace, Greece

S **Lomov** Katholieke Universiteit Leuven, Belgium

J W S **Longhurst** University of the West of England, UK

G **Loo** The University of Auckland, New Zealand

J **Lourenco** Universidade do Minho, Portugal

J E **Luco** University of California at San Diego, USA

H **Lui** State Seismological Bureau Harbin, China

C J **Lumsden** University of Toronto, Canada

L **Lundqvist** Division of Transport and Location Analysis, Sweden

T **Lyons** Murdoch University, Australia

Y-W **Mai** University of Sydney, Australia

M **Majowiecki** University of Bologna, Italy

D **Malerba** Università degli Studi di Bari, Italy

G **Manara** University of Pisa, Italy

B N **Mandal** Indian Statistical Institute, India

Ü **Mander** University of Tartu, Estonia

H A **Mang** Technische Universitat Wien, Austria,

G D, **Manolis,** Aristotle University of Thessaloniki, Greece

W J **Mansur** COPPE/UFRJ, Brazil

N **Marchettini** University of Siena, Italy

J D M **Marsh** Griffith University, Australia

J F **Martin-Duque** Universidad Complutense, Spain

T **Matsui** Nagoya University, Japan

G **Mattrisch** DaimlerChrysler AG, Germany

F M **Mazzolani** University of Naples "Federico II", Italy

K **McManis** University of New Orleans, USA

A C **Mendes** Universidade de Beira Interior, Portugal,

R A **Meric** Research Institute for Basic Sciences, Turkey

J **Mikielewicz** Polish Academy of Sciences, Poland

N **Milic-Frayling** Microsoft Research Ltd, UK

R A W **Mines** University of Liverpool, UK

C A **Mitchell** University of Sydney, Australia

K **Miura** Kajima Corporation, Japan

A **Miyamoto** Yamaguchi University, Japan

T **Miyoshi** Kobe University, Japan

G **Molinari** University of Genoa, Italy

T B **Moodie** University of Alberta, Canada

D B **Murray** Trinity College Dublin, Ireland

G **Nakhaeizadeh** DaimlerChrysler AG, Germany

M B **Neace** Mercer University, USA

D **Necsulescu** University of Ottawa, Canada

F **Neumann** University of Vienna, Austria

S-I **Nishida** Saga University, Japan

H **Nisitani** Kyushu Sangyo University, Japan

B **Notaros** University of Massachusetts, USA

P **O'Donoghue** University College Dublin, Ireland

R O **O'Neill** Oak Ridge National Laboratory, USA

M **Ohkusu** Kyushu University, Japan

G **Oliveto** Universitá di Catania, Italy

R **Olsen** Camp Dresser & McKee Inc., USA

E **Oñate** Universitat Politecnica de Catalunya, Spain

K **Onishi** Ibaraki University, Japan

P H **Oosthuizen** Queens University, Canada

E L **Ortiz** Imperial College London, UK

E **Outa** Waseda University, Japan

A S **Papageorgiou** Rensselaer Polytechnic Institute, USA

J **Park** Seoul National University, Korea

G **Passerini** Universita delle Marche, Italy

B C **Patten,** University of Georgia, USA

G **Pelosi** University of Florence, Italy

G G **Penelis,** Aristotle University of Thessaloniki, Greece

W **Perrie** Bedford Institute of Oceanography, Canada

R **Pietrabissa** Politecnico di Milano, Italy

H **Pina** Instituto Superior Tecnico, Portugal

M F **Platzer** Naval Postgraduate School, USA

D **Poljak** University of Split, Croatia

V **Popov** Wessex Institute of Technology, UK

H **Power** University of Nottingham, UK

D **Prandle** Proudman Oceanographic Laboratory, UK

Materials Characterisation IV

Computational Methods and Experiments

Editors

A.A. Mammoli
University of New Mexico, USA

C.A. Brebbia
Wessex Institute of Technology, UK

 **WIT**PRESS Southampton, Boston

Editors:

A.A. Mammoli
University of New Mexico, USA

C.A. Brebbia
Wessex Institute of Technology, UK

Published by

WIT Press
Ashurst Lodge, Ashurst, Southampton, SO40 7AA, UK
Tel: 44 (0) 238 029 3223; Fax: 44 (0) 238 029 2853
E-Mail: witpress@witpress.com
http://www.witpress.com

For USA, Canada and Mexico

Computational Mechanics Inc
25 Bridge Street, Billerica, MA 01821, USA
Tel: 978 667 5841; Fax: 978 667 7582
E-Mail: infousa@witpress.com
http://www.witpress.com

British Library Cataloguing-in-Publication Data

A Catalogue record for this book is available
from the British Library

ISBN: 978-1-84564-189-4
ISSN: 1746-4471 (print)
ISSN: 1743-3533 (on-line)

The texts of the papers in this volume were set individually by the authors or under their supervision. Only minor corrections to the text may have been carried out by the publisher.

Preface

Materials science in recent years has undergone rapid development in part as a consequence of advances in our ability to control and design at very small scales. Nanotechnology is seen as the new frontier in materials, with the promise of performance and functionality far exceeding today's standards. Many "conventional" materials are also benefiting from improvements in our ability to characterize them and better understand their behavior, often leading to incremental performance enhancements.

Characterization has by necessity kept pace with the development of new materials. In many cases, the characterization of complex behavior is made indirectly by the use of a model coupled with experimental data. In other cases, physical testing provides data to tune model parameters. The first part of the book is dedicated to the computational model – experiment interaction. Later sections contain a range of classical testing methods applied to innovative materials and composites, new testing methodologies, and two sections dedicated to cements and construction materials.

We note that many of the challenges that face society as a consequence of diminishing resources, especially energy, will in part be met by better materials, which ultimately should be designed and used with sustainability in mind.

We are confident that the conference will foster fruitful exchanges of ideas, which the book will extend to a wider audience still. The contents of this book reflect the quality of the submissions and the diligence of the reviewers, whom we wish to thank.

The Editors
New Forest, 2009

Contents

Section 1
Computational models
and experiments

Identification of material properties of FRC using coupled modeling

P. Procházka, A. Kohoutková & J. Vodička
CTU Prague and Association of Civil Engineers, Prague, Czech Republic

Abstract

In this paper identification of material properties in the vicinity of reinforcement of FRC is based on coupled modeling. It consists of the mutual comparison of experimental and mathematical models with the aim of obtaining a more accurate estimate of stresses in experiments and more reliable input data in the mathematical treatment. As the measurements on site are very expensive, experiments simulating the system of the concrete-surrounding medium are prepared in scale models in stands (basins with a glazed front side and a length of 2-6 m), where physically equivalent materials substitute the real ones. Based on similarity rules, very good agreement with reality is attained. Typical applications are found in tunnel construction and reinforcement of slopes using recycled reinforced concretes (waste of bricks and used concrete serve as an aggregate in new built concretes). In order to identify the most exacting location in the concrete, coupled mechanical pullout tests are carried out together with chemical analysis conducted by Raman spectroscopy. It appears that the extent of ettringite on the interface fiber-surrounding matrix plays a very important role, and also other minerals occurring there can influence the interface situation, but less than the ettringite. In the numerical treatment a useful trick is applied, which stems from the idea of generalization of temperature effects – eigenparameters. They describe the plastic behavior as well as the damage at the interfaces. Their applications in the paper will be the most important element of the creation of the coupled model.
Keywords: coupled modeling, fiber reinforced concrete, recycled aggregate, chemo-mechanical analysis, eigenparameters; application: slope reinforcement.

1 Introduction

Fibers play a very important role, particularly during the curing process of concrete, as they suppress local cracking and warping in the composite structure

WIT Transactions on Engineering Sciences, Vol 64, © 2009 WIT Press
www.witpress.com, ISSN 1743-3533 (on-line)
doi:10.2495/MC090011

and avoid the possibility of corrosion of reinforcing steel rebars. On the other hand, polypropylene fibers can display other advantages. If aggregate from recycled material (shattered bricks or concretes) are used in the concrete mixture, they essentially increase the toughness of the material and can be applied to the elements that are in tension. It also appears that after mobilization of the fibers, even higher peak stresses can be safely attained. A very important fact follows from numerous experimental studies: since the steel fibers increase the protection of complete concrete against flaws, the fibers in recycled concrete increase the tensile bearing capacity of the material. The pullout problem was carried out for both materials, as a chemo-mechanical analysis explained certain reasons of the behavior in both types of materials: classical concrete reinforced by stiff fibers and concrete recycled with polypropylene fibers. Convergence analysis for determining cohesion and tensile strength is proposed and eventually a nano-mechanical measurement based on Raman microscopy is introduced.

The testing machine MTS Alliance RT/30 was used for carrying out the mechanical tests. From the combination (coupling) of experimental and theoretical methods the possibility of looking into the heart of the problem, the interfacial fiber-concrete mechanical and chemical properties, is enabled. The interfacial mechanical characteristics are involved in the angle of internal friction and cohesion. With these mechanical characterizations the chemical spectra and, consequently, the description of chemical elements and minerals, express the connection of nano- chemo- and mechanical properties.

2   Experiments with classical concrete

The testing machine MTS Alliance RT/30, see Fig. 1, is used for the pullout tests that are carried out for the purpose of this study. It is an electromechanical tool for compressive, tensile, and bending tests of materials. The maximum compressive and tensile force is 30kN. The size of the possible samples is 150 x 150 x 250 mm (width x length x height). The velocity of loading was in our case 0.04 mm/minute.

The scheme of the container in which the fiber-concrete aggregate samples have been tested is depicted in Fig. 2. In the container the cement paste with one fiber symmetrically positioned in the aggregate is cured. Six samples have been tested. The results in time of curing are given in Fig. 3. The experiment was prepared with a high quality of preparation of cement paste and the positioning of the fiber was also extraordinarily accurate. The results of this study testify to this, as the variance is very small. Fig. 4 shows the appropriate graph obtained from statistical averaging of the previous results.

We would probably be interested in the reason why the steel reinforced concrete loses its bearing capacity during the curing process. The answer may follow from the chemical test descriptions that are presented in the next section. In the case the steel fibers, or other polymerized fibers used in a humid milieu, similar results can be expected. The peak stresses are attained not at the end of the curing and hardening process of concrete, but early in the beginning. Our interest is concentrated exactly on the time interval when the mixture loses its water contents and this is the moment of the highest admissible stress.

WIT Transactions on Engineering Sciences, Vol 64, © 2009 WIT Press
www.witpress.com, ISSN 1743-3533 (on-line)

Figure 1:   Testing machine.

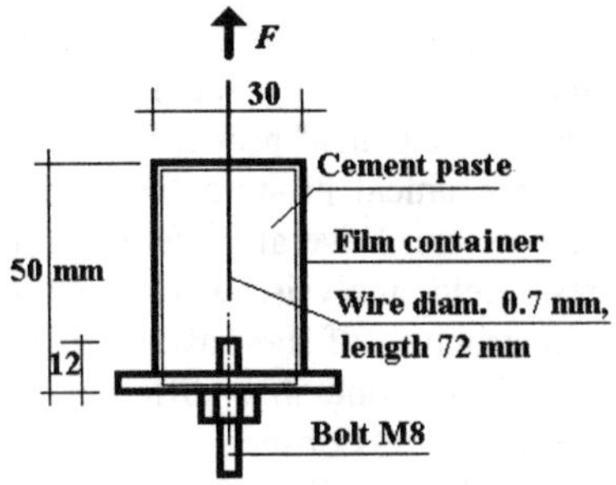

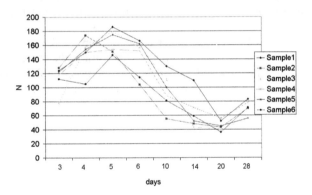

Figure 2:   Scheme of the tested samples.

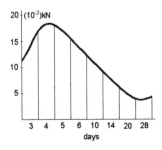

Figure 3:   Admissible forces for six samples at the time of concrete curing.

Figure 4:   Resulting average admissible forces at the time of concrete curing.

3 Raman spectroscopy of cement–steel interfaces

As mentioned above, it is widely accepted that the mechanical behavior of composites is highly dependent on the interface between the fiber and the matrix. The interface exists at some area around the fiber surface, where the local properties, including the morphological features, chemical compositions and thermo-mechanical properties, begin to change. The range of the microstructure and mechanical property gradients within the interface is from nanometers to micrometers. Several different test methods, such as the Raman spectroscopy stress field analysis, were used to investigate the interface properties. The microstructure of the paste matrix in the vicinity of the transition zone of the fibers is considerably different from that of the bulk paste away from the interface. It was observed that the transition zone in the mature composite is rich in $Ca(OH)_2$, usually in direct contact with fiber surface, and is also quite porous, making it different from the microstructure of the bulk paste. The $Ca(OH)_2$ layer is about 1 μm thick and resembles the duplex films. Pullout tests were carried out for chemical and mechanical characterization of the bonding. It was found that frictional as well as anchoring effects controlled the pullout resistance of the straight fibers.

The application of Raman ad infrared spectroscopy in the field of cement and concrete chemistry are quite significant. Measuring the relative intensity of Raman peaks associated with C_3S and calcium hydroxide followed the progress of the reaction. These data sets show that a change in the hydration mechanism occurs at about 13 hours.

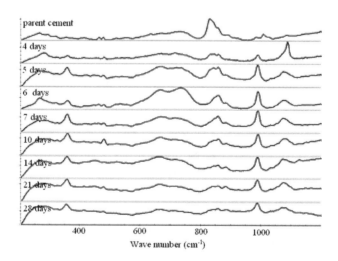

Figure 5:   Raman spectra of the hydrated Portland cement during 0 to 28 days.

Raman microspectroscopy chemical mapping has been used in this work, both for the monitoring of Portland cement hydration during 28 days and for spectroscopic analyses of differences in chemical composition of the interface area around the steel fiber surface in comparison with the surrounding bulk cement matrix composition (Fig. 5).

The five micrometer steps were selected for microspectroscopic mapping and the whole mapping area was 450 x 450 micrometers. The average spectrum has been computed from the set of measured mapped spectra. The hydration process is represented by a set of chemical equations describing the hydration of the main cement phases C_3S, C_2S, C_3A and C_4AF (the nomenclature used here for cement is $C=CaO$, $S=SiO_2$, $H=OH$, $A=Al_2O_3$, $F=Fe_2O_3$, $\hat{S}=SO_4$). Raman microspectroscopy has been used as a powerful technique for the analysis of the hydration cement products, e.g. $Ca(OH)_2$ and ettringite ($C_6A \ \hat{S}_3H_{32}$). Fig. 6 shows the Raman spectra of the hydrated Portland cement at 0 to 28 days period. The increasing intensity of $Ca(OH)_2$ and ettringite and decreasing of the C_3S and C_2S, respectively, is distinct. These chemical properties are probably the prevailingly reason for the decrease of the bearing capacity of the fibers imbedded in the concrete.

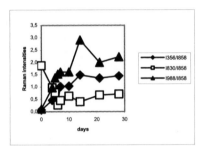

Figure 6:   Changes in the relative abundance of $Ca(OH)_2$ (I_{356}/I_{858}), C_3S (I_{830}/I_{858}) and ettringite (I_{988}/I_{858}) versus days of the cement hydration.

4   Recycled concrete and polypropylene fibers

Among promising structural concretes one also can include ones that are created from recycling materials. They can substitute and spare the natural resources of gravel aggregates. Using additional scattered synthetic fibers, the structure of concrete is stiffened and former brittle material becomes ductile, which shows both high tensile strength and ductility. For concrete mixer creation, clean and unclean brick rubbish (waste) was used, i.e. structural rubbish in the second case contained imparted pieces of bricks, pore-concrete blocks, face bricks, floor tiles, ground concrete, backfill, and so on.

The strength of the materials strongly depends on the amount of cement. The following are certain material properties for various mixtures measured against the standard concrete M20:

a) brick-concretes with lower amount of cement (denoted as C1T)
- tensile strength at bending   5.24%
- compressive strength   10.24%
- strength in transversal tension   13.50%

b) brick-concretes with higher amount of cement (denoted as C2H)
- tensile strength at bending   7.98%
- compressive strength   16.27%
- strength in transversal tension   19.47%

Denotation C3T and C4H refers to the same material properties after 90 days of use. Absolute values of the observed concretes with brick waste aggregates are illustrated in Fig. 7.

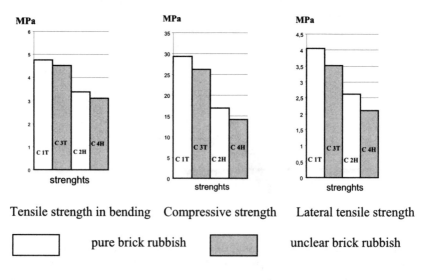

Tensile strength in bending   Compressive strength   Lateral tensile strength

pure brick rubbish   unclear brick rubbish

Figure 7:   Comparison of basic characteristics of brick concretes with fibers.

The strength of brick concrete was lower than that of fine grain concrete, which is an impact of the inactive component, i.e. brick rubbish. Fibers scattered in the structure of brick concrete change the character of classical damage of trial bodies. Fibers also change the values of tensile strengths in bending under reloading by one or two concentrated loads. Last but not least, it is possible to produce the brick concrete without expensive admixtures. For tests on watertight concrete following the standard "Determination of water-tightness of concrete", samples from brick concrete with fibers C3T and C4H from unclean brick rubbish aged 3 months were selected. Three cubes with sides of 150mm were loaded in a watertight box for 24 hours by water pressure 0.1 MPa and then another 24 hours by pressure 0.2 MPa. Leakage through the parallelepipeds attained nearly the upper surface of the cubes and the area of each shattered by lateral tension was more than 90% wet. With respect to the results of the tests, the water-tightness of the brick concrete with fibers is negligible.

For the typical structure of three types of concrete with waste brick aggregate, the pullout test results are seen in Fig. 8. Here the increase of admissible stress is obvious after the polypropylene fibers have been mobilized. A small deviation of force–displacement curves also indicates relatively reliable samples prepared for these tests.

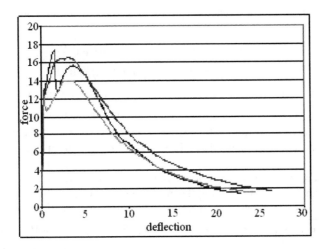

Figure 8:   Diagram force (kN) deflection (mm) for recycled concrete.

5   Mathematical formulation for the coupled modeling

Because of the shape of the samples, the axisymmetric problem is solved. The displacements are described by a vector function $\boldsymbol{u} \equiv \{u_r, u_\theta\}$ of the variable $\boldsymbol{x} \equiv \{r, \theta\}$. The traction field on the interfaces or boundaries is denoted as $\boldsymbol{p} \equiv \{p_r, p_\theta\}$. Assuming the "small deformation" theory, it may be satisfactory to formulate the essential contact conditions on the interface as follows (no penetration conditions):

$$[u]_r = u_r^c - u_r^a \leq 0 \qquad \text{on } \Gamma_C \tag{1}$$

where Γ_C is the interfacial boundary between the fiber and the matrix, u_r^c is the outward normal (radial) displacement of the fiber at a current point and u_r^a is the same displacement at an adjacent point inside the concrete matrix on the interfacial boundary Γ_C. Similarly we define

$$[u]_t = u_t^c - u_t^a \leq 0 \qquad \text{on } \Gamma_C \tag{2}$$

At each adjacent point on the interface $\bar{p}_{p_r} \leq p_+$ has to be valid, where p_+ is the tensile strength and $\bar{p}_{p_r} = p_r + \delta_r$, where δ_r is an internal parameter. Similarly introduce $\bar{p}_{p_t} = p_t + \delta_t$, where δ_t is another internal parameter. In this way, in the radial direction Fischera's conditions should be fulfilled:

$$[u]_r \leq 0, \quad p_+\kappa(p_+ - p_r) - p_r \geq 0, \quad \{p_+\kappa(p_+ - p_r) - p_r\}[u]_r = 0 \qquad (3)$$

where κ is the Heaviside function. In the tangential direction it should be valid that:

$$c\,\kappa(p_+ - \bar{p}_r) - \bar{p}_r \tan\varphi - |\bar{p}_t| \geq 0, \quad |[u]_t| \geq 0,$$
$$\{c\,\kappa(p_+ - \bar{p}_r) - \bar{p}_r \tan\varphi - |\bar{p}_t|\}|[u]_t| = 0 \qquad (4)$$

where $\tan\varphi$ is the tangent of the internal friction of both materials (Coulomb friction), τ_b is the shear strength or cohesion, both being given material coefficients that are different for different coupled materials on contact. These conditions describe the generalized Mohr-Coulomb law involving the exclusion of tension.

We concatenate the above conditions and generalize them to obtain a realistic model of the interfacial behavior. Then, the problem can be formulated in terms of penalties as coefficients of constraint (side conditions). Setting

$$\bar{p}_r = k_r[u]_r, p_r = k_r[u]_r - \delta_r, \text{ and } \bar{p}_t = k_\theta[u]_\theta, p_t = k_t[u]_t - \delta_\theta, \qquad (5)$$

where k_r, k_θ are normal spring and tangential spring stiffnesses. The extended Lagrange principle provides (Γ is the external boundary and $a_s(u, u)$ is the bilinear form of the system fiber concrete matrix):

$$\Pi = \frac{1}{2}\sum_{s=1}^{2} a_s(u, u) - \int_\Gamma \bar{p}^{\mathrm{T}} u\, dx +$$
$$+ \int_{\Gamma_C}\{k_r([u]_r)^2 + k_r[u]_r |[u]_t| + k_t([u]_t)^2\}\, dx -$$
$$- \int_{\Gamma_C}\{(p_+)\kappa(p_+ - \bar{p}_r)[u]_r + c\,\kappa(p_+ - \bar{p}_r)|[u]_t|\}\, dx \qquad (6)$$

Note that the spring stiffnesses k_r, k_t play the role of penalty. The problem can also be formulated in terms of Lagrangian multipliers, which then leads to mixed formulation. The latter case is more suitable for a small number of boundary variables; the problem looked at here decreases the number of unknowns introducing the penalty parameters.

6 Coupled modeling

Considering the external boundary conditions and the material constants are given, the main objective here is to adopt the numerical results and the experimental conclusions. One possible approximation is the assumption that formulates the transformation formulas for interfacial forces. In the example presented hereinafter, the normal internal parameters δ_r are assumed too small in comparison to the real tractions and the tangential internal parameters are selected in such a way that $\delta_t = ap_t$, where the coefficient is to be determined from the condition: calculated external energy is equal to measured external energy.

As the assumption applied here is in fact very simple, the algorithm is easy. Calculate the response of the force applied in real situation and compare the results expressed in terms of external energy. Since most probably they will not be equal, calculate the internal parameter. This is not easy in this case as the relations between internal parameters and the energy are not linear. On the other hand, a smart algorithm can be used, such as the steepest descent or Raphson iteration. The material properties are selected as: $E_f = 170$ GPa, $E_m = 17$ GPa, $v_f = 0.3, v_m = 0.16$. The radius of the fiber is 0.6 mm, the coefficient of Coulomb friction is 0.23 and the shear bond strength is 43.5 kPa.

Sample results are depicted in Fig. 9. It is seen that the normal tractions do not principally change, but the shear tractions are basically improved by the optimization. The optimal appears to be $a = 1.76$.

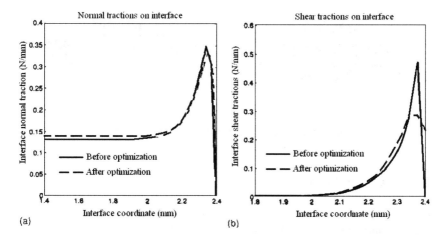

Figure 9:   Interface tractions

7   Possible application in increasing slope stability

In this section the aim is focused on possible application of the recycled composite material in geomechanics. The reinforcement of slopes is very important in certain cases of extensive objects, deposits from open pit mines, tailing dams and such. If not stiffened, they occupy large areas of agricultural lots, or lots for dwelling buildings. In Fig. 10 the influence of nails from the material under consideration principally improves the slope stability. The distribution of vertical displacements for unreinforced (left picture) and reinforced (right picture) are depicted. Principal shear stresses with marked possible slip curves also illustrate the improvement of the stability situation using reinforcement by the recycled material (FRP). The final pictures are drawn in hypsography, which enables one to realize the stability situation before and after reinforcement. An unstable slope obviously turns to be stable when reinforcement is applied.

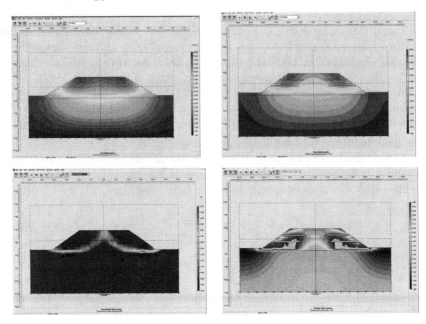

Figure 10:   Displacements and principal shear stresses in unreinforced (left) and reinforced (right) slope.

8   Conclusions

In this paper chemical and mechanical properties are applied for investigation of contact zones in fiber reinforced concrete. The chemical treatment has been carried out by Raman microspectroscope, while the mechanical properties have been derived from results conducted in cylindrical samples (pullout test). It was shown that the results from both approaches should be observed simultaneously. Coupled modeling proved to be a powerful means for understanding the material behavior of the composite systems. Examples of practical applications of stiff and weak fibers have been presented.

Acknowledgements

The financial support of GAČR, project number 103/08/1197 is appreciated. The research has also been supported by a grant from the Ministry of Education of the Czech Republic number MSM6840770001,5.

A micromechanical model and numerical simulation of framework interstice concrete

Q. G. Yang, Z. J. Yi, X. B. He, Y. H. Ma, F. Huang & C. H. Zhao
Civil Engineering and Architecture School,
Chongqing Jiaotong University, P.R. China

Abstract

Being a kind of framework material, framework interstice concrete is composed of single-grade or gap-grade aggregate which are bonded by cement or bitumen, whose structural characteristic is "bonding crunode + aggregate + space". This paper develops a kind of micromechanical model, carrying out numerical simulation of flexual performance of the framework interstice concrete. The calculating results basically conform to the experimental result gained in the laboratory. The method discussed in the paper can be developed to apply in calculating analysis on all kinds of framework interstice concrete materials.

Keywords: framework interstice, framework interstice concrete materials, micromechanical model, numerical simulation.

1 Introduction

To accomplish a pavement's service functions, such as water permeability and noise reduction, framework interstice concrete material has been recently used more and more in pavements. In the perspective of its internal structure, cement or asphalt cementitious matter is used to bond single-grade or gap-graded aggregate to form a "bonding crunode + aggregate + space" internal framework structure. The framework formed by aggregates and elastic nodes endows materials with strength and deformation properties, and the connective space allows for its water permeability and noise reduction functions; therefore, framework interstice concrete material is a new kind of pavement material with good performance.

WIT Transactions on Engineering Sciences, Vol 64, © 2009 WIT Press
www.witpress.com, ISSN 1743-3533 (on-line)
doi:10.2495/MC090021

Because of the existence and processing of inner structural space, it is difficult with this kind of material to build finite-element models and to simulate its mechanical performance.

Currently a variety of concrete micromechanical models have been established to research the relationship of concrete's micro-formation and its macro properties. In article by Tang [1], a plane model is used to analyze the concrete's properties. In the micro-models, the author considers the concrete as consisting of three sorts of materials – cement materials, aggregate and interface materials. When setting up models, the aggregates in fixed size are stochastically scattered in a certain plane area; the gaps among the aggregate are filled with cement material and the surface material with a certain depth is added as the third type of material outside the aggregate. The models were efficient to simulate the fracture process, especially when cracks emerge from the interface. For the properly-designed framework interstice concrete materials, cracks usually emerge in the bonding material, so there is no need for the third-phase material. In addition, it is hard to deal with the spaces in these models.

Adler et al. [2] proposes a method to deal with concrete internal voids from the viewpoint of geometry, but still much work needs to be done to build mechanical models. Articles [3–5] present a method of simulating the mechanical properties of asphalt bituminous concrete with the lattice model. In the micro lattice model, the aggregates are simplified as rigid joints, and the interaction of asphalt membrane among aggregates is replaced by a bar, whose mechanical parameter is gained by analyzing the asphalt membrane, and then a lattice structure can be established to simulate the performance of asphalt concrete. The advantage of the lattice model is that there is no need to consider the concrete's internal space and it's feasible to simulate the mechanical properties of concrete. But apparently, this kind lattice model cannot get the aggregate's influence on the property of the concrete, meanwhile, it cannot efficiently check the stress state of the bonding material. To some extent the performance of framework interstice concrete is decided by the bonding material, so both to investigate the stress state of the bonding material and to investigate the relationship between the bonding material and the whole concrete are important.

In order to research the performance of framework interstice concrete, this paper develops a micromechanical model, which can easily consider the spaces in framework interstice concrete and the effect of the aggregates. Based on the micromechanical model, the simulation results conform to that gained in the laboratory. The advantage of the method mentioned in the paper is that the study result of the stress state of bonding materials can guide the design of framework interstice concrete.

2 The calculating principle

Static finite element numerical calculation is to disperse the structure space and make displacement interpolation at the discrete nodes.

$$u_i(x,y,z) = \sum_{I=1}^{n} N_I(x,y,z)u_{iI} \tag{1}$$

$i = 1,2,3$ are indicators of spatial coordinates. $I = 1,2,...n$ are finite element node; U_{iI} is the first element node in i direction displacement, $N_{1(x,y,z)}$ is the first element of Lagrange interpolation function. We use elastic-plastic constitutive equation to calculate. The unit of the constitutive equation is written in form of matrix, geometric equation,

$$\varepsilon = Lu \tag{2}$$

physics equation,

$$\sigma = D\varepsilon \tag{3}$$

balance equation,

$$L^T\sigma + q = 0 \tag{4}$$

stress boundary condition,

$$L_n^T\sigma = p \tag{5}$$

displacement boundary condition,

$$u = \overline{u} \tag{6}$$

elastic strain,

$$\left\{\varepsilon^{el}\right\} = \frac{\sigma^e}{E\varepsilon^e}\left\{\varepsilon^{nl}\right\} \tag{7}$$

plastic strain,

$$\left\{\varepsilon^{pl}\right\} = \left\{\varepsilon^{nl}\right\} - \left\{\varepsilon^{el}\right\} \tag{8}$$

elastic-plastic matrix,

$$\left[D_{cp}\right] = \frac{\sigma^e}{E\varepsilon^e}\left[D_c\right] \tag{9}$$

The elastic matrix of aggregate is gained by inserting anisotropic stress-strain relationship into isotropic materials. It can be expressed as:

$$[Dc] = \frac{E}{(1+v)(1-2v)}\begin{bmatrix} (1-v) & v & v & 0 & 0 & 0 \\ v & (1-v) & v & 0 & 0 & 0 \\ v & v & (1-v) & 0 & 0 & 0 \\ 0 & 0 & 0 & \frac{(1-2v)}{2} & 0 & 0 \\ 0 & 0 & 0 & 0 & \frac{(1-2v)}{2} & 0 \\ 0 & 0 & 0 & 0 & 0 & \frac{(1-2v)}{2} \end{bmatrix} \tag{10}$$

$\left\{\varepsilon^{nl}\right\}$ is the general strain vector, $\left\{\varepsilon^{el}\right\}$ is strain vector. $\left\{\varepsilon^{pl}\right\}$ is plastic strain vector, $\left[D_c\right]$ is elastic matrix, $\left[D_{cp}\right]$ is plastic matrix, L is differential operator, D is rigid matrix, q is volume force vector, p is surface force vector.

3 The micromechanical model of framework interstice concrete

3.1 Geometric model

This article adopts a plane model to simulate the mechanical properties of the framework interstice concrete.

Because the framework interstice concrete's features and force carrying characteristic are dependent on its inner structural constitution "aggregate + elastic nodes + void", in general, the aggregate size of the framework interstice concrete only influences the space size, but little to the main performance of the framework interstice concrete.

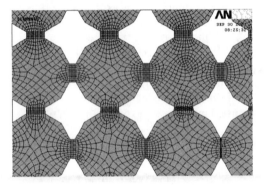

Figure 1:   The shape and arrangement of aggregate and bonding material.

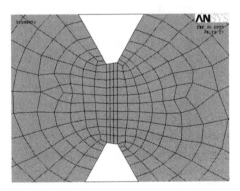

Figure 2:   The mesh of aggregate and bonding material.

During calculations, when the bonding material is more cured, the aggregate can be simplified to a single size. In the model, the aggregate shape is treated as a twelve-edged polygon with same long sides for the convenience of modeling (Figure 1). Accordingly, the gaps between two aggregates are filled with bonding material evenly.

The advantages of this kind of modeling are: when the aggregate is simplified, the aggregate's adjacent edges are straight, and it is easy to get bonding material mesh without an abnormal unit (Figure 2); moreover, the other gaps which are not filled with bonding material left on the geometry can be regarded as the natural spaces of the framework interstice concrete to achieve the physical similarity (Figure 1). In this way, one can focus more on the bonding material in the calculation, at the same time, pay attention to the relationship between the bonding mechanical parameter and the overall performance of framework interstice concrete.

3.1.1 Aggregate

Aggregate size: diameter unified as 5mm. In practice, framework interstice concrete usually adopts gap-graded or single-graded aggregate; considering the focus of the calculation is to find the bonding's effect on the overall performance of the framework interstice concrete and to simplify the model, the aggregate size is unified as 5mm which is near to the actual size. Meanwhile the smaller the aggregate size is, the more convenient to get befitting mesh of the two different materials—aggregate and bonding material.

Aggregate shape: when the aggregate is simplified as circular, the circle of two aggregates will lead abnormal mesh and stress singularity (Figure 1, 2). Therefore, it is simplified into a twelve-edged polygon with the same surface.

3.1.2 Bonding material

The bonding thickness between aggregate is 0.1-0.5mm according micro-measure. In usual, the bonding thickness is 0.5mm, so in the model the bonding material thickness is chosen as 0.5mm (Figure 2).

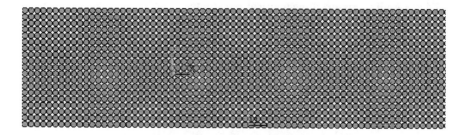

Figure 3:   The overall model of framework interstice concrete.

3.1.3 The overall model

Aggregate is in a parallel arrangement and only the gaps between two adjacent parallel edges are filled with bonding material (Figure 1, 2), while the other parts aren't filled, the rest of the parts simulating the natural spaces.

These two kinds of materials in accordance with the planar combination eventually form 10×40 (cm) planar pieces (Figure 3) so that we can compare the results with the 10×10×40 (cm) bending experimental test.

3.2 Unit analysis

Unit type: because of the difficulties and the feasibilities of the three-dimensional model, we choose the plane model which can consider thickness for analysis. ANSYS' PLANE42 is able to establish two dimensional entity structural models. The unit can be used as both a plane unit and axisymmetric unit. At the same time the unit can deal with plasticity, creep, large deformation and large strain problems. The overall model of framework interstice concrete has 1,109,723 units and 1,182901 nodes.

3.3 The model mesh

Bonding material: it can be divided into three units in thickness, ten units in length, and the unit's ratio between width and length is 1/5, that accord with the basic requirement of units (Figure 2).

The aggregate: the adjacent part of aggregate and bonding coordinates with the bonding material's unit, while other parts divide by themselves according to the principle of adapting. Aggregate and its units dividing is illustrated in Figure 1.

3.4 Material mechanical parameter

3.4.1 Aggregate's mechanical parameter

The aggregate material used in the test is granite, whose elastic modulus is 50-85GPa. According to the test and related test data, the elastic modulus in the calculation is 60Gpa. Granite Poisson's ratio is between 0.20 and 0.30 in test, and it is 0.27 in the calculation. Granite Stress-strain relationship is linear.

3.4.2 Bonding material mechanical parameter

In this paper, the bonding material used in the test is polymer cement material, whose parameters are from the actual test data in the laboratory. The following figures are two representative curves of the polymer cement measured in the test.

Through experiments, it is found that the bonding material elastic modulus is between 7000~8000Mpa (Figure 4). So it is 7500Mpa in the calculation

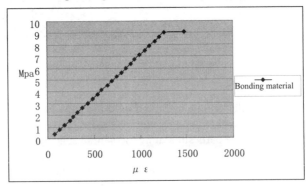

Figure 4:   Bonding material stress-strain curves from experiments.

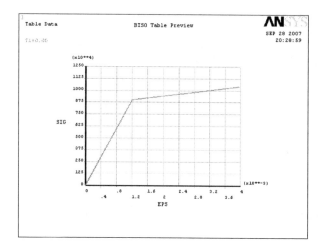

Figure 5:   Bonding material stress-strain curves in the calculation.

(basically one degree lower than that of aggregate) and the Poisson's ratio is 0.23. According to experiments its stress-strain relationship is chosen as typical dual line (Figure 5).

The first segment of the straight line, as in the test: the yield stress can be looked on as 9Mpa, and we choose the straight line before the stress reaches 9Mpa; the second segment: it is a little slope so as to avoid the dis-convergence.

3.5 Boundary condition and loading

Linear loading is adopted in the calculation. Loading location and the supporting condition is in accordance with that in the experiment (Figure 6).

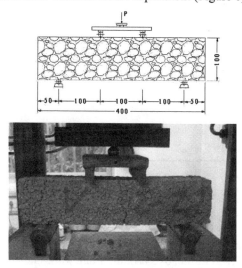

Figure 6:   Schematic diagrams of loading (unite: mm) and loading photo.

3.6 Solution method

The paper adopts Newton-Raphson method to solve the equations. The finite element formulation of Newton-Raphson divides the entire load-displacement process into a series of incremental segments; and in each increment, the structure's loading response is nearly as linear. Besides, after each increment's load is increased, structural tangent stiffness matrix would be modified many times according to the required status variable to eliminate the unbalanced force and make sure that the calculation results satisfy the given precise requirement. And then considering the status as the equilibrium state, we continue to act on the loading increment to get incremental displacement by solving linear algebraic equations.

4 Calculation results analysis of framework interstice concrete

4.1 The simulated results of flexural test

After the simulated flexural specimen, which is loaded according to Figure 6, the framework interstice concrete's mid-span load-displacement curve is gained. (Figure 7.)

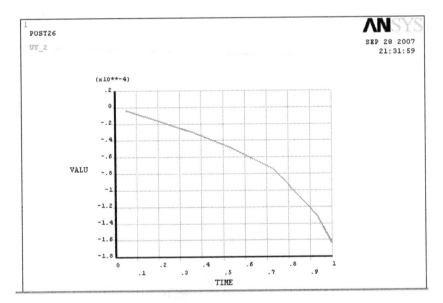

Figure 7: Framework interstice concrete's mid-span load-displacement curve.

The calculated curve shows when the load is added to 14.6KN (the load is two times of TIME STEP in ANSYS), the framework interstice concrete appears yielding, at this time, the corresponding displacement is 0.075mm.

4.2 Experimental results

Figure 8 is an actual measuring stress-strain curve, and in test the measuring point is at mid-span bottom of the concrete beam. From the chart: when the load is increased to 12.3~15.2KN (in the loading as Figure), the concrete stress at mid-span bottom has a specifically relation with loading, $\sigma = PL/(bh^2)$), the framework interstice concrete appears yielding.

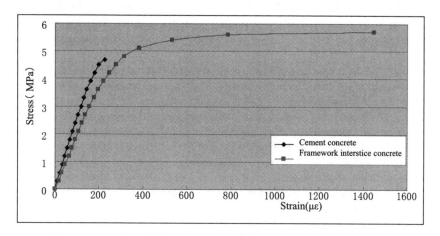

Figure 8:   The representative stress-strain curve of framework interstice concrete (the measuring point is at mid-span, bottom of the concrete beam)

4.3 The comparison of the calculation result and experimental test

Comparing the result of test with that of calculation, the calculation yielded load has 5%~18.7% difference with the actual yielded load in experimental test, but the mid-span displacement has about 30% difference with the actual (it is maybe because the support has local deformation). From the comparison, conclusions can be drawn: the calculation model in the paper can better simulate the framework interstice concrete's mechanical properties.

5 Conclusions

The micromechanical calculation model developed in the paper, with a clear concept and convenient modeling, can better forecast and analyze the mechanical properties of framework interstice concrete, whose calculation results are consistent with that in the laboratory. The method in the paper can further simulate and study the mechanical actions of framework interstice concrete under other loading conditions, and popularize to study the creep of bituminous concrete materials. Henceforth, the model can be further developed into a three dimensional model in order to better simulate framework interstice concrete materials' mechanical features.

Acknowledgements

The study has been supported both by Ministry of Transport of the People's Republic of China through project (2008 318 814 62) and by Chongqing Science & Technology Commission projects, whose support is gratefully acknowledged.

References

[1] Tang C. A., Numerical tests of progressive failure in brittle materials. *Journal of Mechanics and Practices,* 21(2), pp. 21-24,1999.
[2] Adler. P.M, Thovert. J.F, Bekri .S & Yousefian. F, Real Porous Media: Local Geometry and Transports. Fracture. *Journal of Engineering Mechanics /August*, pp. 829-839,2002.
[3] Arslan A., Ince R. & Karihaloo B.L., Improved Lattice Mode for Concrete Fracture. *Journal of Engineering Mechanics/January, pp.* 57-65, 2002.
[4] Gianluca Cusatis, Zdenek P. Bazant & Luigi Cedolin, Confinement-Shear Lattice Model for Concrete Damage in Tension and Compression: I. Theory. *Journal of Engineering Mechanics ASCE*/December, pp. 1439-1448,2003.
[5] Dai Q.L., Martin H. Sadd, Venkit Parameswaran & Arun Shukla, Prediction of Damage Behaviors in Asphalt Materials Using a Micromechanical Finite-Element Model and Image Analysis. *Journal of Engineering Mechanics ASCE/July*, pp. 668-676,2005.

Optimization of a numerical model of three-dimensional heat transfer during friction stir welding of 304L stainless steel

D. Furse & C. Sorensen

Department of Mechanical Engineering, Brigham Young University, USA

Abstract

A numerical model of friction stir welding has been optimized to fit experimental data of three welds of 304L stainless steel at various weld velocities and spindle speeds. Optimization was used to determine the values of six model parameters that describe phenomena during the welding process. The parameter values were then compared to each other and to the default values. Predicted tool slip was determined to vary significantly with differing weld conditions. The coefficient of friction was also shown to vary. The mechanical efficiency of the three welds was predicted to range between 0.80 – 0.90. Optimization of additional welds is suggested so that correlations of the model parameters to weld velocity and spindle speed can be determined.

Keywords: friction stir welding, FSW, optimization, 304L stainless steel.

1 Introduction

Friction stir welding (FSW) is a solid state welding process in which a rotating tool generates heat along the joint interface, resulting in the flow of plasticized material around the tool. Since 1991, when FSW was developed at TWI [1], many models (both analytical and numerical) have been documented. An effective model of FSW can be a valuable predictive tool, allowing researchers to develop the process much more rapidly than could be accomplished through experiments only. Also, a good model of FSW can help researchers come to a better understanding of *how* the process works.

In this paper, a model of friction stir welding developed by Nandan *et al.* [2,3] is explored. The use of the model, which will be referred to as the Penn State model, requires the user to input six parameters that describe various

WIT Transactions on Engineering Sciences, Vol 64, © 2009 WIT Press
www.witpress.com, ISSN 1743-3533 (on-line)
doi:10.2495/MC090031

aspects of the process—a slip constant, a friction constant, a viscous dissipation constant, a mechanical efficiency factor, a "fraction of heat entering the workpiece" factor, and a constant for the heat transfer at the bottom face. These parameters can be difficult or near impossible to measure, so an optimization approach is used to determine the parameter values that will "best fit" the model to experimental data. If the Penn State model is to be used to predict weld behavior, these parameters must be 1) bounded with some confidence and 2) known to what extent they vary with weld velocity and spindle speed. This paper will explore both issues.

2 Description of optimization approach

2.1 Experimental data

The data used to optimize the Penn State model comes from an unpublished work of 11 welds of varying rotational speeds and feed rates performed by Owen [4]. Each weld was performed on a 304L stainless steel workpiece with dimensions 60.96 cm x 20.32 cm x 0.635 cm. The tool used for the welds was a MegaStir Technologies™ E44016 Polycrystalline Cubic Boron Nitride (PCBN) tool. For reference, the welds are given corresponding numbers in Table 1.

The majority of welds will be used in determining the correlation, if one exists, of the model parameters to the weld conditions given. The remaining welds will be used to test the accuracy of the correlation.

Table 1:   Welds performed by Owen [4] and their intended use.

Weld No.	Spindle Speed (rpm)	Feed Rate (mm/s)	Used to determine correlation	Used to validate correlation
1	300	0.423	X	
2	300	0.847	X	
3	300	1.693		X
4	300	2.54	X	
5	400	0.847		X
6	400	1.693	X	
7	400	2.54		X
8	500	0.423	X	
9	500	0.847	X	
10	500	1.693		X
11	500	2.54	X	

Model accuracy is assessed by comparing the predicted temperatures at specific locations in the workpiece with those obtained experimentally. Each workpiece was instrumented with 16 thermocouples distributed as shown in Figure 1, where the y position indicated is the distance from the weld centerline (positive y is the retreating side). All thermocouples were placed at a depth of $z = 3.4$ mm. Spindle torque and forces in all three directions were simultaneously recorded. The most interior thermocouples were placed very close to the stir zone of the tool, but were not displaced during the weld.

By using two thermocouples at identical y locations (but different x locations), Owen was able to show a repeatability error of only ~25°C [4]. This indicated that the steady-state assumption used in numerical models of friction stir welding was suitable for the welds he performed. The repeatability error is also useful for establishing an acceptable level of model accuracy. The model error is given by

$$E = \sum_{i=1}^{n} \left(T_{i,measured} - T_{i,predicted} \right)^2 \tag{1}$$

where $T_{i,measured}$ is the peak temperature measured at location i and $T_{i,predicted}$ is the peak temperature predicted by the model at the same location. Thus, using eqn (1) for n monitoring locations, the model error is not expected to be less than $E = 25^2 n$ or $E = 625n$.

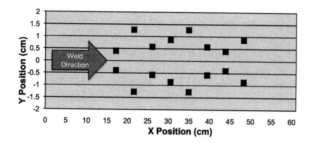

Figure 1:   Locations of thermocouples in workpiece (not to scale) as given in [4].

2.2 Optimization routine

Optimization of the Penn State model is accomplished through the software package OptdesX. The objective of the optimization was to minimize the error function given in eqn (1) by changing the six model parameters previously mentioned. Six monitoring locations are used, with y values corresponding to the thermocouples at -1.27, -0.86, -0.40, 0.40, 0.86, and 1.27 cm. The optimization does not require any constraining functions. Since it is possible that more than one combination of model parameters may yield similar results – in other words, the solution may not be unique – the default values for 304L stainless steel (Table 2) are used as the initial starting points for each optimization routine. This helps to ensure that each search begins by looking for a minimum in the same area. The GRG algorithm within OptdesX was the search algorithm used.

A shell file written for OptdesX controls the flow of information in the process by calculating the model error and updating the values of the analysis variables as directed by OptdesX. The shell file serves as a link between the analysis engine (the Penn State model) and the optimization engine (OptdesX). In this approach, there is not one optimization problem, but rather seven optimization problems, where the welds used for correlation (see Table 1) are optimized. The remaining welds will be used to validate the correlation obtained.

3 Preliminary results

The optimal values for the six model parameters have been determined for Welds No. 1, 4, and 9. They are shown below in Table 2. For Weld No. 1, the default parameters led to a model error of $E = 116,260$, which by eqn (1) and for six monitoring locations corresponds to an average location error of 139°C. Optimization reduced the error to 3,040 (22.5°C) – slightly less than the minimum expected value of 3,750 (25°C). Similarly, Welds No. 4 and No. 9 began with high model errors at the default position (154°C and 113°C, respectively), and ended with lower errors at the optimum position (44°C and 30°C). In each case, the model initially under-predicted the temperatures at all locations, but especially those closest to the weld.

Table 2:   Optimal coefficient values for the welds tested.

Parameter	Default Values	Optimal Values for Welds		
		No. 1	No. 4	No. 9
Slip constant, δ_0	2.0	1.97	3.18	0.77
Friction constant, μ_0	0.45	0.50	0.58	0.46
Viscous dissipation constant, β	0.005	0.005	0.005	0.005
Mechanical efficiency, η	0.8	0.92	0.98	0.8
Fraction of heat entering workpiece, f	0.41	0.584	0.568	0.45
Heat transfer constant at bottom face, h_b	0.004	0.0037	0.0041	0.002

Plotting the predicted peak temperatures at the specified monitoring locations against the data obtained experimentally shows that the model is fairly accurate (see Figure 2). Welds No. 1 and 9 were much hotter than Weld No. 4. This is due to the feed rate in Weld No. 4 being six times higher than in Weld No. 1 and three times higher than in Weld No. 9.

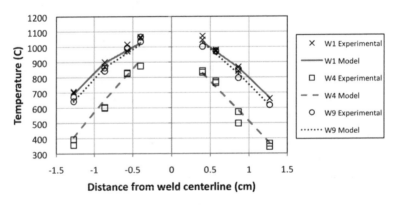

Figure 2:   Peak temperatures in Weld Nos. 1, 4, and 9.

3.1 Slip constant

Slip at the tool-workpiece interface is modelled according to

$$\delta(r) = 1 - \exp\left(-\delta_0 \frac{\omega}{\omega_0} \frac{r}{R_S}\right) \tag{2}$$

where δ is the fraction of slip, ω is the rotational speed of the tool, ω_0 is a reference value of rotational speed, r is the distance from the tool axis, and R_S is the radius of the tool shoulder. The constant δ_0 is the user-adjustable parameter of interest. Thus, the fraction of slip throughout the tool for the welds studied is distributed according to Figure 3. The default value ($\delta_0 = 2.0$) seemed to match closely with the optimal value of 1.97 for Weld No. 1, whereas Weld No. 9 had a significantly lower fraction of slip. This indicates that more sticking occurs at higher spindle speeds, which is a result that was not expected. Further work will demonstrate whether this is a consistent result. Also, the optimal value of slip for Weld No. 4 indicates that higher feed rates may also increase the amount of sticking.

3.2 Friction constant

The optimal friction constant for Weld No. 1, $\mu_0 = 0.5$, was higher than the value chosen by Nandan et al [3] for mild steel. They chose $\mu_0 = 0.4$, and showed that in their case, adjusting the friction constant between 0.3 to 0.5 affected the peak temperature in the plate by about 100 K. Since Owen showed, as mentioned in Section 2.1, that the average error in thermocouple measurement was 25 K, a difference of 100 K is fairly significant.

The friction constant is used to scale the coefficient of friction according to

$$\mu_f(r) = \mu_0 \exp(-\lambda \delta \omega r) \tag{3}$$

where λ is a constant equal to 1 s/m. Since the coefficient of friction is function of two user-adjustable parameters (δ and μ_0), each weld studied had a slightly different shape and scale for the distribution for friction. The friction coefficient for the welds studied is shown in Figure 3. From the distributions of slip and friction shown, it appears that there is a correlation between the two parameters: the higher the friction coefficient, the more slip is present. It is unknown if this relationship only applies to the model, or if it represents real phenomena during FSW of 304L stainless steel.

3.3 Viscous dissipation constant

The viscous dissipation constant β is used in determining the heat generated from plastic deformation, S_b, by the equation $S_b = \beta \mu \Phi$. The function Φ is defined as

$$\Phi = 2\left(\left(\frac{\partial u_1}{\partial x_1}\right)^2 + \left(\frac{\partial u_2}{\partial x_2}\right)^2 + \left(\frac{\partial u_3}{\partial x_3}\right)^2\right)$$

$$+ \left(\frac{\partial u_1}{\partial x_2} + \frac{\partial u_2}{\partial x_1}\right)^2 + \left(\frac{\partial u_1}{\partial x_3} + \frac{\partial u_3}{\partial x_1}\right)^2 + \left(\frac{\partial u_2}{\partial x_3} + \frac{\partial u_3}{\partial x_2}\right)^2 \tag{4}$$

WIT Transactions on Engineering Sciences, Vol 64, © 2009 WIT Press
www.witpress.com, ISSN 1743-3533 (on-line)

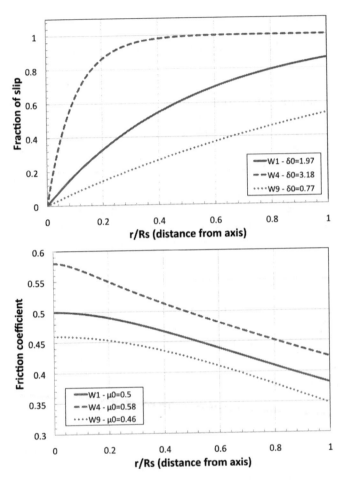

Figure 3: Fraction of slip and coefficient of friction used in the optimization of Welds No. 1, 4, and 9.

Optimization showed that the temperature profile of the workpiece was not sensitive to changes in β. This was anticipated since the heat generated due to viscous dissipation is fairly small. Yet, as Nandan *et al* conclude, without this term, the temperature profile does not vary with respect to changes in viscosity [3].

3.4 Mechanical efficiency

The mechanical efficiency η is used in determining how much heat is generated at the tool-workpiece interface (S_i) according to

$$S_i = \left[(1-\delta)\eta\tau + \delta\mu_f P_N\right](\omega r - U_1 \sin\theta)\frac{A_r}{V} \tag{5}$$

where τ is the shear stress at yielding, P_N is the normal pressure, θ is the tilt angle of the tool, U_l is the weld velocity or feed rate, A_r is any small area on the interface, and V is the control volume enclosing the area A_r.

The model is predicting that mechanical efficiency diminishes as the rotational velocity increases. The change in η from Weld No. 4 to No. 9 was quite significant – a decrease of about 18 percent. Optimizing the other welds will clarify whether this change is solely due to changing the rotational speed or if other factors are contributing.

3.5 Fraction of heat entering workpiece

The fraction of heat entering the workpiece, f, is a parameter that when combined with the mechanical efficiency describes the percentage of power from the FSW machine that is converted into heat in the workpiece. Although the user is free to choose any value for f, Nandan et al [3] suggest using the following equation, which comes from steady-state one dimensional heat transfer from a point source located in the interface of two dissimilar materials at the same temperature [5].

$$f = \frac{J_W}{J_W + J_T} = \frac{1}{1 + \cdot (k\rho c)_T / (k\rho c)_W} \tag{6}$$

Using eqn (6) for a PCBN tool and 304L stainless workpiece, f is calculated to be ~ 40 percent, which is the value chosen by Nandan et al [2] in their study of stainless steel. This is comparable to the optimal values for the welds optimized so far, especially Weld No. 9 ($f = 45$). The welds with slower rotational velocities predicted more heat entering the workpiece.

The fraction of heat entering the workpiece seems to be calibrated low in the model. Eqn (6) assumes that both the tool and the workpiece are at the same temperature, a condition perhaps true towards the end of the plunge phase, but not during the weld, when the tool is moving into much cooler workpiece material. Shercliff and Colegrove state that heat lost into the tool is typically on the order of 10% or less [6]. When combined with the mechanical efficiency, the total predicted amount of power from the machinery entering the workpiece is ηf, which in the welds studied is only $0.35 - 0.55$. Chao et al showed that this "heat efficiency" during FSW of aluminum was about 95 percent, which is much higher than the heat efficiency of traditional fusion welding (60-80%) [7]. However, they noted that the energy in FSW is converted from mechanical energy to heat and deformation, so that the term "heat efficiency" is not quite the same. It is unknown why the Penn State model predicts such a low fraction of heat entering the workpiece.

3.6 Heat transfer constant at bottom face

The heat transfer at the bottom surface ($z = 0$) is modeled as Newtonian cooling under natural convection:

$$k\frac{\partial T}{\partial z}\bigg|_{bottom} = h(T - T_a) \tag{7}$$

where T_a is the ambient temperature. The contact resistance "convection" coefficient h is given by $h = h_b(T - T_a)^{0.25}$ where h_b is our unknown parameter with units equal to cal/cm^2-s-K$^{1.25}$ [8]. Thus, the heat transfer coefficient at the bottom face is a function of the temperature at the face and the constant h_b given by the user. The optimal h_b for Welds No. 1 and 4 stayed close to the default value ($h_b = 0.004$), corresponding to an h value of about 900 W/m^2-K under the tool. Weld No. 9 however, had an $h_b = 0.002$.

Sherdiff and Colegrove have suggested using a spatially variable (rather than temperature variable) heat transfer coefficient due to the different conditions of contact resistance between the workpiece and the backing plate [6]. Below and behind the tool, the contact resistance is low, due to the downward force. Away from the tool, however, the contact resistance is high; the clamping points can be neglected. Thus, the heat transfer constant h_b should not be a function of weld velocity or spindle speed.

4   Conclusion

A method for determining previously unknown parameters in the Penn State model through optimization techniques has been discussed. Results were shown to lead to accurate predictions of workpiece thermal profiles. Because the model is still under development, this method will be helpful in identifying discrepancies between the model and experimental data. It is probably too early to make any definitive statements on how the model parameters should be adjusted with regards to weld velocity and spindle speed. Likewise, although the optimized parameters correspond to material behavior during friction stir welding, statements on the characteristics of 304L stainless steel during FSW would be premature.

Although the use of optimization techniques is a roundabout way of determining the values of model parameters, it has been shown to yield reliable thermal profiles of the workpiece. Optimizing the other welds will allow more concrete statements to be made about model performance and predictions. In addition, correlations of the model parameters will allow the model to be used in a more predictive way, and it will yield further insight into the behavior of 304L stainless steel during friction stir welding.

References

[1] W. M. Thomas, E. D. Nicholas, J. C. Needham, M. G. Church, P. Templesmith, and C. Dawes: Int. Patent PCT/GB92/02203 and GB Patent 9125978-9, 1991.
[2] Nandan, R., Roy, G.G., Leinert, T.J. & DebRoy, T., Numerical modelling of 3D plastic flow and heat transfer during friction stir welding of stainless steel. *Science and Technology of Welding and Joining*, **11(5)**, pp. 526-537, 2006.